Excellence in Word Problems

Year 6

By Richard Cooper

RISING STARS

Rising Stars UK Ltd., 76 Farnaby Road, Bromley,
BR1 4BH

Website: **www.risingstars-uk.com**

Published 2003
Reprinted 2004
Text, design and layout ©Rising Stars UK Ltd.
Editorial: Tanya Solomons
Concept design: Burville Riley
Design: Ken Vail Graphic Design, Cambridge
Illustration copyright ©Louisa Burville-Riley
Cover photo ©Grant Symon/Getty Images

British Library Cataloguing in Publication Data

A CIP record for this book is available from the
British Library.

ISBN 1-904591-22-1

Printed by Wyndeham Gait, Grimsby, UK

Contents

How to use this book   4

All about word problems   6

Place Value   8

Fractions   10

Decimals   12

Percentages   14

Addition   16

Subtraction   18

Money   20

Time   22

Measures   24

Puzzles   26

Patterns and sequences   28

Multiplication   30

Division   32

2D shapes   34

3D shapes   36

Position and direction   38

Data handling   40

Two-step problems   42

Answers   44

How to use this book

The *Excellence in Word Problems* series is designed to help you use your mathematical skills to solve a range a problems, many of which are written in words rather than figures.

Rather than giving a sum like:

4 × 6 = ☐

a word problem might be along the lines of:

"If I have 4 six-packs of cola, how many cans of cola do I have in total?"

The answer is the same, but you need to think about it a bit more and remember to answer by writing or saying: **"I have 24 cans of cola in total."**

The introduction

This section of each page gives you an idea of the sort of problems you are likely to see and helps you to understand what maths you need to use.

20 EXCELLENCE IN WORD PROBLEMS YEAR 6

Money

These problems involve adding, subtracting, multiplying or dividing using money. Don't forget that most of these will be decimal problems too. Remember to put in the '£' or 'p' too!

Hanusia earns £5.25 a week pocket money doing jobs for her mum and dad. She wants to save all her earnings for 12 weeks. How much will she have if she does save for 12 weeks?

Read the question then read it again — '£5.25... 12 weeks... how much?'

Choose the operation/unit of measurement — 12 lots of £5.25... that's multiplication.

Estimate — Round 12 down to 10 and £5.25 down to £5: 10 × £5 = £50

Calculate

£5.25
× 12
£63.00

Hanusia will have £63.

Check — 12 × 5 = £60; 12 × 25p = £3. I am correct!

Hints and tips
- When calculating money problems, always line up the decimal points.
- £0.45p ✗ 0.45p ✗ £0.45 ✔ 45p ✔
- For sums over £1, always put in any missing zeros £1.1 ✗ £1.01 ✔

Hints and tips

The hints and tips section gives you useful ideas for completing the problems on the other page. These are the things you need to remember if you are doing a quiz or test!

The example problem

The flow chart takes you through an example problem *step-by-step*. This is important when answering word problems as it helps you to order your thoughts, do each part of the problem in the right order and *check your work*!

Every problem has the same five steps.
READ the question then read it again
CHOOSE your operations and units
ESTIMATE your answer
CALCULATE
CHECK your answer

We remember this by using this mnemonic:
RED
CLOWNS
ENTER
CAVES
CAREFULLY

MONEY 21

...nusia decides to spend £2.50 a week and save £2.75.
...ow much has she saved after 25 weeks?

Hanusia's dad, Wasim, wants to buy a new garden shed. He saves £35 a week.
How many weeks will he have to save if the shed costs £525?

Hanusia's mum, Januja, has saved £110. She offers to put it towards the shed costing £525. How much more would be needed to pay for the shed?

Hanusia wants to buy some tools for her dad's shed. There is a sale on at the DIY shop: £6.99 for each tool. Hanusia has £40. What is the largest number of tools she can buy? How much change will she get?

Januja wants to buy some packets of seeds. She buys 6 packets of seeds each costing £2.95 and a garden hose to water the seeds for £25. How much does she spend altogether?

...hallenge
...Hanusia and her family are going to live in Italy where the currency is the euro. There are 1.6 euros to the pound. Hanusia's parents sell their house for £129,500. How many euros can they spend on a new house in Italy?

...Jse a written method or a calculator.

£1   €1

The questions

The questions get harder as you go down the page.

- Section 1 questions are fairly straightforward and help you to practise your skills.
- Section 2 questions are a bit harder but will help you to remember all the key points.
- The Challenge sections are really tough and sometimes mean that you can make up games and your own questions! They can be great fun!

All about word problems

Ten top tips for working with word problems

1 *Work step-by-step.* Follow the flow chart.

Red
Clowns
Enter
Caves
Carefully

Read the question then read it again
Choose your operations and units
Estimate your answer
Calculate
Check your answer

2   Always *show your working* or 'method'. This will help you to keep track of what you have done and may help you to get extra marks.

3   Always *include your units* in the answer. If you don't, you won't get full marks.

4 When you first read through a question, *underline important words and numbers*. This will help you to remember the important bits!

5 *Draw a picture* to help you. Sometimes a question is easier if you can 'see' it. Drawing 6 apples can help you if you need to divide them!

6 If the problem has a number of steps, break it down and do *one step at a time*.

7 When *checking your answers*, look at the inverse operation.

8 Sometimes an answer will 'sound right'. Read it out (quietly) and listen. *Does it make sense?*

9 If you are using measurements (grams, litres, cm), make sure that the *units are the same* before you calculate.

10 Once again! *Read the question then read it again.*

Place value

Place value questions will often ask you to make up a large or small number using different digits. Remember, each digit has a different value depending on where you put it.

Amar has five digit cards: six, three, eight, nine and four. He can only use each card once. What is the largest 4-digit number he can make? Write your answer in words.

Read the question then read it again

'Write your answer in words…'

Choose the operation/unit of measurement

I'm ordering the digits. Largest one first.

Estimate

The number will be nine thousand and something.

Calculate

9 then 8 then 6 then 4. The largest 4-digit number Amar can make is nine thousand, eight hundred and sixty-four.

Check

Yes, the number is the largest and it's spelt correctly.

Hints and tips

★ Multiplying by a thousand is the same as multiplying by 10, then by 10 again and by 10 again. For example: 1000 × 2 is the same as 2 × 10 = 20: 20 × 10 = 200: 200 × 10 = 2000

a) What is the smallest 4-digit number Amar can make with his cards? Write your answer in words.

b) What is the second largest 4-digit number Amar can make with his cards? Write your answer in words.

c) What is the second smallest 4-digit number Amar can make with his cards? Write your answer in words.

a) Amar swaps all five of his cards for five *different* digit cards. What is the largest 4-digit number he can make if he only uses each new card once? Write your answer in words.

b) What is the smallest 4-digit number Amar can make if he is allowed to use any three odd digits and one even digit?

Place the digits 9, 4, 7, 6, 5, 1 in the boxes in order to get the largest result.

☐☐ × ☐ + ☐ × = ☐☐

Fractions

Fraction problems are tricky. You might be asked to find a fraction of a number, e.g. 'What is half of 30?' You may also be asked to work out 'What fraction of 30 is 15?'

George spends 39 weeks of the year at work as a teacher and 13 weeks of the year on holiday. What fraction of the year does George spend on holiday?

Read the question then read it again

'What fraction... on holiday...'

Choose the operation/unit of measurement

13 weeks *out of* 52... that's division!

Estimate

52 weeks in a year... a quarter?

Calculate

$\frac{13}{52} = \frac{1}{4}$ George spends $\frac{1}{4}$ of the year on holiday.

Check

Yes, $\frac{1}{4}$ of 52 is 13, which is the same as dividing 52 by 4... which is 13. I was correct!

Hints and tips

★ Finding $\frac{1}{2}$ of something is the same as dividing it by 2; finding $\frac{1}{3}$ of something is the same as dividing it by 3; finding $\frac{1}{4}$ of something is the same as dividing it by 4... etc.
If you want to find $\frac{2}{3}$ of something, find $\frac{1}{3}$ first, then multiply by 2. To find $\frac{3}{4}$ of something, find one quarter first, then multiply by 3 etc.

a) George spends 39 weeks a year at work as a teacher. What fraction of the year is this?

b) Georgina is a part-time teacher. She works for 26 weeks a year as a supply teacher. For what fraction of the year does Georgina work?

c) What fraction of the year does George spend on holiday abroad if his family go abroad for 2 two-week holidays a year?

a) George spends $\frac{3}{10}$ of his 40 day summer holiday preparing lessons and marking books. How many days is this?

b) Georgina travels around the world from August 1st to 31st December. What fraction of the year is this in months?

Challenge

If George spends two-thirds of his 39 weeks at work in the classroom and Georgina spends 11 thirteenths of her 26 weeks at work in the classroom, who spends the most time in class and by how much?

Decimals

Decimal problems can be about distance or time. Don't forget to add the units! These questions use addition and subtraction but watch out for the Challenge!

At the school Sports Day, Kamilah came second in the long jump with a leap of 2.7 m. Lauren jumped 350 mm further and won. How far in metres did Lauren jump?

Read the question then read it again	'2.7 m… 350 mm… how far?'
Choose the operation/unit of measurement	Addition and metres.
Estimate	The answer will be more than 3 metres but it must be realistic.
Calculate	2.7 m = 270 cm 350 mm = 35 cm 270 cm + 35 cm = 305 cm Lauren jumped 3.05 m.
Check	305 cm − 35 cm = 270 cm. I'm correct.

Hints and tips

★ When dealing with mixed decimals such as 2.3 and 1.74, add any missing zeros to make ordering or calculating much easier.
e.g. 2.3 + 1.74 becomes *2.30* + 1.74

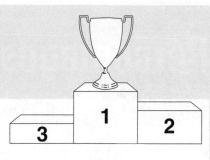

a) Kamilah threw the discus 11.8 m. This was 600 mm further than Lauren.
How far in metres did Lauren throw the discus?

b) Lauren ran the 200 m in 30.9 seconds. Kamilah was 1.2 seconds faster.
What was Kamilah's time for the 200 m?

c) Kamilah cleared 1.61 m in the high jump. Marie jumped 150 mm less.
How high in metres did Marie jump?

a) Grant, Oprah and Lisa played in a basketball tournament. Grant took
28.12 seconds to shoot 8 baskets. Lisa was 3.58 seconds quicker than
Grant but 2.35 seconds slower than Oprah. What was Oprah's time in seconds?

b) Grant, Oprah and Lisa also ran in the school cross country race. This time Grant
was 240 seconds faster than Oprah who finished in 25.5 minutes. Lisa was 600 seconds
slower than Oprah. How much faster was Grant than Lisa?

Challenge

All five children formed a tug of war team. This is how much each of them weighed.

Grant 46.83 kg, Lisa 35.27 kg, Lauren 41.59 kg, Marie 44.42 kg, Oprah 46.80 kg

They won three matches in a row before losing in the final to a team that was 5500 g
lighter than them. How heavy were the winning team? Give your answer in kg.

Percentages

Percentage problems are usually about money. Some questions ask for a percentage of an amount of money, e.g. 10% of £1. Other questions might ask you to work out 10% off a price.

Jordan wants to buy a new pair of trainers. A pair of 'Reeburks' are priced at £35 but are on special offer with 20% off the price. How much would Jordan pay for the trainers now?

Read the question then read it again	'£35… 20% off… how much?'
Choose the operation/unit of measurement	Percent means 'out of a hundred'. The units are £.
Estimate	20% is the same as a fifth…
Calculate	10% of 35 = 3.5 so 20% = 7. £35 − £7 = £28 Jordan would pay £28 for the trainers.
Check	28 + 7 = 35

Hints and tips

★ Learn these percentage/decimal/fraction equivalents (equivalent means 'the same').

$1\% = 0.01 = \frac{1}{100}$ $10\% = 0.1 = \frac{1}{10}$ $20\% = 0.2 = \frac{1}{5}$

$25\% = 0.25 = \frac{1}{4}$ $50\% = 0.5 = \frac{1}{2}$ $75\% = 0.75 = \frac{3}{4}$

★ You can find percentages by halving and quartering. For example, 12.5% of £48,000

50% = £24,000 25% = £12,000

12.5% = £6,000

a) Jordan's dad Steve goes to the sports shop. He sees a pair of socks at £3.
At the till he is offered a 30% discount because it is an end of season sale.
How much would Steve pay?

b) Jordan's sister Stacey wants to have tennis lessons. The normal price is £20
per hour but during Wimbledon there is an amazing 60% off! How much is a
tennis lesson during Wimbledon?

c) Jordan joins the local athletics club. The cost of membership is £300 per year
with 70% off for under 16s. Jordan is 11. How much does he pay to join for a year?

a) Stacey is trying to choose a new coat for Christmas. She sees the same
coat in two places. At the supermarket the coat is £70 with a 30% discount.
In the department store the coat is £50. Which one should she buy? What
is the difference in price?

b) Steve's golf lessons have gone up! They used to cost £12 per lesson
but are up by 20%. How much does Steve pay for a golf lesson now?

Challenge

Steve, Jordan and Stacey have £1300 saved in the bank. Steve takes out 70%, Jordan
takes 10% and Stacey takes 15% to spend on holiday. They each come home with 10%
of their spending money left. How much does each of them have when they get home?

Addition

Most of these addition problems ask you to add two 3-digit numbers. That can be tricky. Remember to line up the numbers accurately in the sum – then you will be fine.

Charlie and Tony collect crisp packet labels for their school. Charlie has 5834 and Tony has 2183. How many do they have altogether?

Read the question then read it again

'5834… 2183… altogether…'

Choose the operation/unit of measurement

'Altogether' means add.

Estimate

5834 is close to 5800, 2183 is close to 2200.
5800 + 2200 = 8000

Calculate

$$\begin{array}{r} 5834 \\ + 2183 \\ \hline 8017 \end{array}$$

Charlie and Tony have 8017 crisp packet labels.

Check

I'll check using the inverse method.
8017 − 5834 = 2183
Also, 8017 is very close to my estimate.

Hints and tips

★ 'increase by' 'how many altogether' 'add'
'what is the total of…' 'find the sum of…'
All these terms and phrases mean ADDITION.

a) Josh has 2472 crisp packet labels and Luke gives him 1320 that his Gran had saved for them. How many labels does Josh have in total?

b) Luke has 1760 crisp packet labels. He increases his collection by 1348. How many labels does he have now?

c) Amy and Ivy start collecting. Amy has 1549 crisp packet labels and Ivy has 1468. What is the sum of Amy and Ivy's collection?

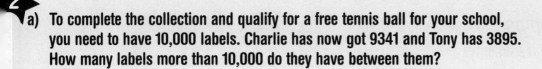

a) To complete the collection and qualify for a free tennis ball for your school, you need to have 10,000 labels. Charlie has now got 9341 and Tony has 3895. How many labels more than 10,000 do they have between them?

b) Amy has 1549 crisp packet labels but Ivy gets bored of collecting and gives her 1468 labels to Amy. Charlie and Tony have got their tennis ball so they give all their spares [see question 2(a)] to Amy. How many labels does Amy have now? Does she qualify for a tennis ball?

Challenge

Josh sets Luke a challenge. Josh shows Luke a grid of 16 squares.

Luke must place a crisp packet label on the first square then double the number of labels on each square until he has filled the grid. How many labels would there be on the sixteenth square? How many tennis balls could he get? [see question 2(a)]

What if the grid was 5 x 5? How many labels would there be on the twenty-fifth square?

How many tennis balls would he get now?! You may need extra paper for this one.

Subtraction

These subtraction problems are taking away a 4-digit number from another 4-digit number. Estimating first will help you get these right.

Rochelle and Mary played pinball in the amusement arcade by the seaside. Rochelle scored 5395 points and Mary scored 3228 less than Rochelle. How many points did Mary score?

Read the question then read it again	'5395… 3228… less than…'
Choose the operation/unit of measurement	'Less than' means subtract.
Estimate	Rounding method… 5400 − 3200 = 2200
Calculate	5395 − 3228 = 2167 Mary scored 2167 points.
Check	2167 + 3228 = 5395 Also, 2167 is close to my estimate.

Hints and tips

★ 'less than' 'difference' 'decrease' 'subtract' All these terms and phrases mean SUBTRACTION.

★ When subtracting 4-digit numbers, make sure you line up the digits in the sum carefully.

★ Always check your answer by using addition.

a) Ivan and Billy played a game of pinball. Billy scored 6467 fewer points than Ivan who scored 8821. How many points did Billy score?

b) Billy got his own back on the 'Virtual Space Ranger' game! He scored 8462 points and Ivan scored 2836 less. How many did Ivan score?

c) Rochelle and Mary tried the same game. Mary scored 1427 and Rochelle scored 9588. What was the difference between the two scores?

a) Mary bought herself, Joe, Hannah and Jonathan 'kiss me quick' hats costing £2.70 each. How much change did she get from a £20 note?

b) Rochelle, Mary, Ivan and Billy had a game of 'Tecken 4'. The girls scored 8725 points. The boys scored 1753 less. Ivan scored 4281 points. How many did Billy score?

Challenge

Here are some famous dates in history.

1963 – President Kennedy assassinated
1815 – Wellington defeats Napoleon at Waterloo
1564 – The birth of Shakespeare

1909 – First flight across the English Channel
1666 – The Great Fire of London
3500 BC – Stonehenge is built

Write down the current year (2003, 2004 etc).
Can you work out how many years ago these events took place?

Money

These problems involve adding, subtracting, multiplying or dividing using money. Don't forget that most of these will be decimal problems too. Remember to put in the '£' or 'p' too!

Hanusia earns £5.25 a week pocket money doing jobs for her mum and dad. She wants to save all her earnings for 12 weeks. How much will she have if she does save for 12 weeks?

Read the question then read it again

'£5.25… 12 weeks… how much?'

Choose the operation/unit of measurement

12 lots of £5.25… that's multiplication.

Estimate

Round 12 down to 10 and £5.25 down to £5: 10 × £5 = £50

Calculate

$$\begin{array}{r} £5.25 \\ \times\ \ \ 12 \\ \hline £\,63.00 \end{array}$$

Hanusia will have £63.

Check

12 × 5 = £60; 12 × 25p = £3. I am correct!

Hints and tips

★ When calculating money problems, always line up the decimal points.

★ £0.45p ✗ 0.45p ✗ £0.45 ✔ 45p ✔

★ For sums over £1, always put in any missing zeros. £1.1 ✗ £1.01 ✔

1

a) Hanusia decides to spend £2.50 a week and save £2.75.
How much has she saved after 25 weeks?

b) Hanusia's dad, Wasim, wants to buy a new garden shed. He saves £35 a week.
How many weeks will he have to save if the shed costs £525?

c) Hanusia's mum, Januja, has saved £110. She offers to put it towards the shed
costing £525. How much more would be needed to pay for the shed?

2

a) Hanusia wants to buy some tools for her dad's shed. There is a sale on at the
DIY shop: £6.99 for each tool. Hanusia has £40. What is the largest number
of tools she can buy? How much change will she get?

b) Januja wants to buy some packets of seeds. She buys 6 packets of seeds each
costing £2.95 and a garden hose to water the seeds for £25. How much does
she spend altogether?

Challenge

Hanusia and her family are going to live in Italy where the currency is the euro.
There are 1.6 euros to the pound. Hanusia's parents sell their house for £129,500.
How many euros can they spend on a new house in Italy?

Use a written method or a calculator.

£1   €1

Time

Time problems can ask you to work out how many minutes there are between two times. They can also ask you to work out what time is 30 minutes later than, say, 13:00. Remember the 24 hour clock!

Kieron and his friends are visiting 'Chunder Towers' amusement park for a birthday treat. They arrive at 09:43 and stay until 16:52. How long do they stay at the park?

Read the question then read it again

'09:43... 16:52... how long?'

Choose the operation/unit of measurement

Counting on. It's addition... hours and minutes.

Estimate

9 count on to 16 = 7 hours

Calculate

09:43 + 7 hours = 16:43
plus 9 minutes = 16:52
They stay for 7 hours and 9 minutes.

Check

My answer is close to my estimate of 7 hours.

Hints and tips

★ 1 millennium = 1000 years

★ 1 century = 100 years

★ 1 decade = 10 years

★ 1 year = 12 months or 52 weeks or 365 days

★ 1 leap year = 366 days ('Olympic years' are leap years: 2004, 2000, 1996, 1992 etc.)

★ 1 week = 7 days

★ 1 day = 24 hours

★ 1 hour = 60 minutes

★ 1 minute = 60 seconds

a) Kieron wants to go on the 'Water Chute'. He begins queuing at 10:45 and gets on the ride at 11:02. How long does he have to queue?

b) Kieron, Adam and Ronnie all want to have a go at panning for gold in 'Thunder River'. They start panning at 11:27 and finish at 12:10. How long do they pan for gold?

c) The boat trip starts at 12:10 and lasts for 55 minutes. At what time do Kieron, Ronnie and Adam finish the trip?

a) Kieron and his friends have lunch at 13:15. They have to wait 9 minutes for their hotdogs to cook, queue 14 minutes at a stall for some drinks and spend 23 minutes eating and drinking. At what time do they finish eating and drinking?

b) At 14:05 the 'Wild Frontier Rodeo Show' begins! The show is made up of a 16 minute sing-a-long, 19 minutes of lasso tricks, 25 minutes of horse-riding stunts and 11 minutes of cowboys on 'bucking broncos'. At what time does the show end?

 Challenge

Kieron's, Ronnie's and Adam's birthdays are on January 5th, March 14th and May 12th. Can you work out how many days it is to their birthdays from today's date?

How many days is it until your birthday?

Measures

Measures questions can be about weight, capacity or length. Add, subtract, multiply or divide to get the answers. Remember to put in the units!

Triptonfell Rugby club has a pot containing 325 litres of spicy parsnip soup for the spectators. One cup of soup is 200 ml. How many spectators can have a cup of spicy parsnip soup?

Read the question then read it again

'325 litres… 200 ml…'

Choose the operation/unit of measurement

How many *lots of* 200 ml in 325 litres?

Estimate

How many 200 ml in *1 litre* first of all?

Calculate

1 litre = 1000 ml. 1000 ml ÷ 200 ml = 5 so 325 × 5 = 1625. 1625 spectators can have a cup of soup.

Check

325 divided by 0.200 = 1625

Hints and tips

★ When calculating kg and g or l and ml, it helps if you convert the units so they are the same.
e.g. 2 kg + 500 g
convert to 2000 g + 500 g

★ 'Milli' means a thousand in Latin. 1000 years in a millennium, 1000 mm in a metre.
'Kilo' means a thousand in Greek. 1000 g in a kilogram, 1000 m in a kilometre.
'Centi' means a hundred in Latin. 100 cm in a metre, 100 cl in a litre, 100 years in a century.

a) The rugby pitch is 75.5 m long. The groundsman lengthens it by 575 cm.
How long is the pitch now in metres?

b) Brendan's kicking boot weighs 400 g. If all the team's boots weigh the same,
how much do 12 kicking boots weigh?

c) Brendan can kick a rugby ball 28 m. Brendan's coach can kick a ball $2\frac{1}{4}$ times further.
How far can the coach kick the ball?

a) Brendan passes the ball 5.84 m to Stephen. He kicks the ball a further
24.65 m up the pitch. How many centimetres has the ball travelled?

b) Triptonfell Rugby club orders 5000 litres of shandy. It sells an average of
125 litres per day. How long does its supply of shandy last?

 Challenge

Two teams of 15 hungry players eat sandwiches and cakes
after the match. Each player eats 450 g of sandwiches
and 375 g of cakes.
How many kilograms of food are eaten by the teams?

Puzzles

Number puzzles are great fun but you have to think step-by-step to get them right! It can really help to underline key words in these questions.

Who am I? I have three digits and I am less than 130.
I can be divided exactly by 3 and 8.

Read the question then read it again

I need to work methodically…

Choose the operation/unit of measurement

Dividing 3-digit numbers by 3 and 8.

Estimate

As it can be divided by 8 and under 130 it must be…
104, 112, 120 or 128

Calculate

The only number out of those that can be divided by 3 is 120. I am 120!

Check

Double-check my answer…
I am correct.

Hints and tips

★ When solving puzzles it helps to work 'methodically'. This means taking things step-by-step. Test your ideas.

★ Sometimes drawing pictures can help you to solve the problems.

1

a) Who am I? I am a 2-digit number. The sum of my digits is 6.
My units digit is 2 times my tens digit.

b) Fatma is thinking of a 3-digit odd number. The hundreds digit is 3 times
more than the units digit. The sum of the three digits is 4.
What number is Fatma thinking off?

c) Who am I? I have three digits. I can only be divided by myself
and one. The sum of my digits is 11. I am under 150.

2

a) The ages of Alan and Martin add up to 99. Alan's age is Martin's age reversed.
How old are Alan and Martin?

b) All my underpants are red except two. All my underpants are blue except two. All my
underpants are pink except two. How many underpants do I have?

Challenge

Rachel opened her Maths book and found that the sum of the facing pages was 245.
What pages did she open the Maths book to?

Patterns and sequences

Pattern questions might ask you to find the 'nth' number in a pattern or to work out how many numbers are in the pattern. These questions are all about comets.

Halley's Comet last crossed our skies in 1986. The time before that was 1910 and the time before that was 1834. When do you think Halley's Comet will appear again?

Read the question then read it again

> 'Comets?'

Choose the operation/unit of measurement

> I'm looking for the *difference between* the years.

Estimate

> The year 2050?

Calculate

> The difference between the years is 76.
> 1986 + 76 = 2062
> I think Halley's Comet will reappear in 2062.

Check

> Yes, those years fit the sequence of the comet appearing every 76 years.

Hints and tips

★ When asked to predict the next number in a sequence, start looking at the rest of the numbers and how they relate to each other. Work out their differences.

Questions

1

a) Halley's Comet appears every 76 years. The next appearance of Halley's
Comet will be in 2062. When will the next three appearances be after that?

b) Halley's Comet appeared before the battle of Hastings in 1066.
When were its next three appearances?

c) When were its previous three appearances before 1066?

2

a) How many appearances from Halley's Comet can we expect in the next 500 years?

b) The comet Denning-Fujikawa was discovered in 1879. It can be seen every 9 years.
Its next appearance will be in 2005. How many times has it been seen since its
discovery and this current year?

Challenge

Comets are named after the people who first discover them. Write down a two digit number.
This is how often your 'comet' appears. Ask a friend to give you a date from any time in the
last 1000 years. Calculate how many times your 'comet' has been sighted since that date.
Try with 3-digit numbers and longer passages of time.

Multiplication

Multiplication problems are story problems. They are often about measures or money. The key is to work out what numbers you are multiplying and add the units!

Bella has 24 apple trees on her farm. She picks 168 from each one to make some apple pies. How many apples has she picked?

Read the question then read it again

'24 trees... 168 from each...'

Choose the operation/unit of measurement

24 *lots of* 168... multiplication

Estimate

Round 24 down to 20...
$20 \times 170 = 3400$

Calculate

$$\begin{array}{r} 168 \\ \times\ \ 24 \\ \hline 4032 \end{array}$$

Bella has picked 4032 apples.

Check

4032 is fairly close to my estimate. Also, $4032 \div 24 = 168$.

Hints and tips

★ 'times' 'multiply' 'multiplied by' 'lots of' 'product'
All these words and phrases mean MULTIPLICATION. Learn them.

★ If you are asked to 'find the product of these two numbers' make sure you multiply them – don't add them!

a) Bella sells 382 apple pies for 65p each. How much in total does she sell all the pies for?

b) Bella has 52 boxes of cherries each containing 250 g of cherries. How many kilograms of cherries does she have?

c) Bella sells the boxes of cherries for 75p a box. How much does she get for selling all 52 boxes?

a) Bella's farm is doing well. Bella makes £630 for 30 weeks of the year and £450 a week for 22 weeks of the year. How much does Bella make over the course of the year?

b) The farm starts selling different sorts of fruit pies. Bella sells 624 cherry pies, 472 plum pies and 283 apple and raspberry pies. The pies are now sold at 95p each, but they each cost Bella 27p to make. How much profit does Bella make when she sells all the pies?

 Challenge

Bella starts a 'pick-your-own' business on her fruit farm. She charges £2.99 per kilogram of strawberries picked. Max picks 18 kg and Judy picks 42 kg! How much do Max and Judy have to pay altogether?

Division

These division problems are all about a brand new band! Work out which number to divide (the bigger one usually). Don't forget to put in the units! Watch out! There are some big numbers here!

The latest boy band, 'Boyz-U-Really-Prefer' or 'B.U.R.P.', as they are known, are holding a concert. Their fan club of 432 screaming girls are packed equally onto 24 mini-buses to get to the concert. How many girls are there on each mini-bus?

Read the question then read it again	'432… 24 mini-buses… how many girls on each?'
Choose the operation/unit of measurement	24 *into* 432. That's division.
Estimate	20 into 400 = 20
Calculate	$\begin{array}{r} 18 \\ 24\overline{)432} \end{array}$ There are 18 girls on each mini-bus.
Check	My estimate was close. I'll check using the inverse method. 18 × 24 = 432. I was correct!

Hints and tips

★ Remember, multiplication is the opposite of division. Use it to check your answers.

Questions

1

a) B.U.R.P. are playing at Wembley Arena, which holds 5000 people.
How many coach-loads of 50 fans can fit inside?

b) Twelve fans pay a total of £960 for front row seats and backstage passes.
How much do they pay equally between them?

c) Sixteen fans paid a total of £720 for autographed hankies used by the band!
How much did each fan pay equally for an autographed hankie?

2

a) B.U.R.P. went on tour. They played 25 songs at every concert. Each concert
lasted $2\frac{1}{2}$ hours. How many minutes did each song last on average?

b) B.U.R.P. eventually became unfashionable and ended up playing at children's birthday parties.
They charged £87.50 for an afternoon's performance. There were seven members of the band.
They split the money equally. How much did each of them get for a children's party?

Challenge

Use a calculator for this one.

At the height of their fame, B.U.R.P. made £1,000,000! However... this was divided
between the seven members of the band. Each member's share was then taxed at 50%.
Each member then had to pay 50% of what was left to their agent and then 50%
of what was left again to the record company. Another 50% was deducted to
cover expenses. How much did each member end up with?

2D shapes

These questions all ask you to add shapes together and work out what the new shape is. If it helps you can draw each of the questions step-by-step.

Raymond has a number of regular polygons (shapes). All the polygons have sides that are the same length as each other. He experiments by sliding shapes together to make new ones.
He always lines up the sides so that they meet exactly.

Raymond slides an equilateral triangle next to a square to form a new shape. What is the name of the new shape?

Read the question then read it again

Read slowly and carefully...

Choose the operation/unit of measurement

I need to visualise the shapes in my mind...

Estimate

A pentagon of some sort?

Calculate

I see a 5-sided shape – an irregular pentagon. The new shape is an irregular pentagon.

Check

I can draw the shape myself to check.

Hints and tips

 Use a ruler when drawing shapes.

 Picture the shapes in your head.

 Remember the language.

Questions

a) Raymond puts two equilateral triangles together. How many sides does the new shape have?

b) Amber has a go. She puts three equilateral triangles together. What is the name of this new shape?

c) Amber and Raymond take one more equilateral triangle and add it to Amber's shape. What two shapes can they make? How many sides does each have?

a) Raymond starts using more shapes. He takes a hexagon and places an equilateral triangle flush on each of the hexagon's sides. How many sides does this new shape have?

b) Amber makes a shape that looks like a sunflower! She takes an octagon and slides a square onto each of the octagon's sides. How many sides does the 'sunflower shape' have?

 Challenge

Set yourself a time limit to unscramble these shape related words.
Any you don't understand, look up in the glossary.
Under five minutes – you're in great shape!

x	h	e	p	t	a	g	o	n	l	a	w	e	r	y
p	f	b	a	d	p	e	n	t	a	g	o	n	p	u
y	g	h	p	a	z	q	d	i	a	g	o	n	a	l
i	k	s	d	r	b	u	j	s	z	m	c	e	r	r
s	e	c	j	k	c	i	r	c	l	e	t	q	a	h
q	u	a	d	r	i	l	a	t	e	r	a	l	l	o
u	i	l	e	a	q	a	t	r	a	d	g	p	l	m
a	v	e	t	u	o	t	k	i	t	e	o	o	e	b
r	u	n	g	r	h	e	x	a	g	o	n	l	l	u
e	q	e	g	d	z	r	u	n	o	h	l	y	o	s
s	o	r	e	c	t	a	n	g	l	e	c	g	g	c
t	p	a	r	a	l	l	e	l	e	f	s	o	r	l
b	m	u	i	s	o	s	c	e	l	e	s	n	a	j
f	a	b	u	t	r	a	p	e	z	i	u	m	m	h

3D shapes

3D shape questions will often ask you to recognise a range of 3D shapes and count them. This activity is a tricky one, so work step-by-step.

This is the Space Port of 'X-Ellence' which has just experienced a terrible earthquake!

Space school

Passenger terminal

SKYWALKER HOTEL

DOCKING BAY

Have a close look at how it was built and see if you can answer the questions on page 37.

Hints and tips

★ 3D shapes have 'faces' (the flat parts) 'edges' (the long sharp parts) and vertices (the short sharp parts where the edges meet).

vertex

edge

face

a) What is the name of the two shapes either side of the passenger walkway?

b) Name the two shapes you can see in the spacecraft landing area.

c) What is the shape of the docking bay?

a) How many faces does the Space School have and what is the name of the shape?

b) How many faces can you see on the Skywalker Hotel and how many cubes are needed to repair it so that it is restored to a cube shape?

Complete this table to show the total number of each shape in X-Ellence City Space Port.

Shape	cubes	cuboids	square-based pyramids	spheres	hemispheres	cylinders
Number						
Shape	cones	prisms	tetrahedrons	polyhedrons	octahedrons	dodecahedrons
Number						

Position and direction

Alan and Charlie are planning a new garden design. They complete their design on squared paper. These questions are all about the new garden design.

Use the garden plan on page 39 to answer these questions.

The points (–3, 6), (–3, 3) and (3, 6) are three of the four vertices of the swimming pool. What are the coordinates of the fourth vertex?

Read the question then read it again	I need to work step-by-step.
Choose the operation/unit of measurement	I'm working with coordinates…
Estimate	Remember, along then up or down.
Calculate	Find the coordinates already given. Identify the missing one on the grid. It is (3, 3). The coordinates of the fourth vertex of the swimming pool are (3, 3).
Check	Take the time to double-check.

Hints and tips

★ Coordinates mark where the lines cross, not the spaces in between.

✓ right ✗ wrong

★ Remember, 'x' comes before 'y' in the alphabet. Always go ALONG the corridor then UP the stairs.

1

a) What are the coordinates of the four vertices of the barbeque?

b) If Alan was at the point (−2, 4) and Charlie was at the point (1, 5) what would they probably be doing?

c) What are the coordinates of the two seating areas?

2

a) Alan decides that the lawn needs developing. He wants it reflected symmetrically using the y axis as the mirror line. What would be the coordinates be of the four new vertices?

b) Charlie decides to build a dining area in a position that reflects the barbeque using the y axis as the mirror line. What would the coordinates be of the four new vertices?

 Challenge

Use squared paper. Draw an x and y axis using all four quadrants. Design your own garden or playground. Plot the coordinates of the vertices of the main features and write three word problems for a friend to answer.

Data handling

Data handling questions will ask you to look at a chart, graph or table and use the data to answer the questions. Sometimes you will have to transfer data from a table to a chart.

Top of the Pops did a survey to find out the ages of fans who said that the ancient rock group 'Led Balloon' were their favourite band.

What is the most common age of the fans who said Led Balloon were their favourite band?

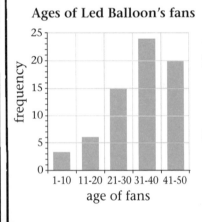

Ages of Led Balloon's fans

Read the question then read it again

> I need to understand what the chart is telling me...

Choose the operation/ unit of measurement

> The chart is telling me the frequency of the grouped ages of Led Balloon fans.

Estimate

> I have to look at all the information that is given to me.

Calculate

> The column showing the highest frequency is the fourth one, which is 31–40. The most common age for a Led Balloon fan is between 31 and 40.

Check

> I can compare my answer with all the other possibilities – yes, I'm correct.

Hints and tips

★ Always look at the titles of the graph and the axes first. They tell you what the information is trying to show.

a) Which age group of fans said Led Balloon were their favourite band the least number of times?

b) Which age group appeared fifteen times in the survey?

c) How many times did the 41–50 age group say that Led Balloon were their favourite band?

a) How many people over 30 said Led Balloon were their favourite?

b) How many Led Balloon fans did Top of the Pops survey altogether?

Challenge

Top of the Pops did another survey. This time they wanted to investigate the ages of fans who said that the teen idol 'Gareth Goats' (he's just a kid) was their favourite pop star.

Sketch a graph showing how you think the ages in the second survey would be shown. Write three questions about your graph for a friend to answer.

Two-step problems

Two-step problems need you to think carefully and keep notes of each step. You will have to complete an operation, take the answer and do a further one or two operations to that answer to get the final answer.

Brights Park Primary are holding their Summer Fête. There are 67 stalls, 33 are selling things and half of the remainder are sideshow games. How many stalls are sideshow games?

Read the question then read it again

'67... 33... half of the remainder...'

Choose the operation/unit of measurement

Subtract 33 from 67 then *divide* the answer by 2.

Estimate

70 – 30 = 40. $\frac{1}{2}$ of 40 = 20... 20 seems reasonable.

Calculate

67 – 33 = 34 *then* half of 34 = 17. 17 stalls are sideshow games.

Check

These are short calculations. I can redo them quickly to check.

Hints and tips

★ Work out which part of a multi-step problem needs to be done first. Always show your working when writing down how you tackled a problem. Work methodically.

a) Courtney and John are running the homemade cake stall. Courtney sells £39 worth of cakes and John sells £45 worth. They give £30 to the school and keep the rest for themselves. How much money do Courtney and John keep?

b) Cathy buys 5 strips of raffle tickets and Harrison buys 4 strips of raffle tickets. The raffle tickets cost 75p a strip. How much do they spend on raffle tickets altogether?

c) Nicky and Tim are selling 'penny sweets'. They started with 1600 sweets. Nicky sells 865 and Tim sells 667. How many sweets are left? How much do they make in £ and pence?

a) Marlon and Ayden are running the 'throw wet sponges at the teacher' stall. Marlon charges 35p per sponge and makes £19.60 and Ayden charges 45p per sponge and makes £20.70. How many sponges were thrown?

b) Paul and Mel are running the 'Lucky Dip' stall. By the end of the fete they have made £157 for the school and £33 for themselves. However, before they go home, Mel suggests they donate 15% of their total takings to her favourite charity. Paul agrees. How much do they give to the charity?

Challenge

Rose and Rene are running the 'Hook a duck' stall. Rose asks Rene, 'If two ducks are swimming in front of another duck, two ducks are swimming behind another duck, and one duck is swimming between two other ducks, what is the minimum number of ducks we can have?' Rene doesn't know! Do you?

Answers

Place value

a) Three thousand, four hundred and sixty-eight
b) Nine thousand, eight hundred and sixty-three
c) Three thousand, four hundred and sixty-nine

a) Seven thousand, five hundred and twenty-one
b) One thousand, two hundred and fifty-seven

Challenge
$74 \times 65 + 1 \times 9 = 43299$

Fractions

a) $\frac{3}{4}$

b) $\frac{1}{2}$

c) $\frac{1}{13}$

a) 12 days

b) $\frac{5}{12}$

Challenge
George spends longer in the classroom by four weeks.

Decimals

a) 11.20 m
b) 29.7 seconds
c) 1.46 m

a) 22.19 seconds
b) 14 minutes

Challenge
209.41 kg

Percentages

a) £2.10
b) £8
c) £90

a) She should buy the coat from the supermarket because it's £1 cheaper.
b) £14.40

Challenge
Steve has £91, Jordan has £13 and Stacey has £19.50.

Addition

a) 3792
b) 3108
c) 3017

a) They have 3236 labels more than the 10,000 they need.
b) Amy has 6253 labels so she doesn't qualify for a tennis ball!

Challenge
First part: 32,768 labels and 3 tennis balls
Second part: 16,777,216 labels and 1,677 tennis balls

Subtraction

a) 2354
b) 5626
c) 8161

a) Mary got £9.20 change

b) Billy scored 2691

Challenge

From 2003 the answers are: 40, 94, 188, 337, 439, 5503

Money

a) She has saved £68.75

b) 15 weeks

c) £415

a) Hanusia can buy 5 tools and keep £5.05 change.

b) £42.70

Challenge

They have 207,200 euros to spend.

Time

a) Kieron queues for 17 minutes

b) 43 minutes

c) 13:05

a) 14:01

b) 15:16

Challenge

Variable answers

Measures

a) 81.25 m

b) 4.8 kg

c) 63 m

a) 3049 cm

b) 40 days

Challenge

24.75 kg of food is eaten by the teams

Puzzles

a) 24

b) 301

c) 137

a) 54 and 45

b) 3

Challenge

122 and 123

Patterns and sequences

a) 2138, 2214 and 2290

b) 1142, 1218 and 1294

c) 990, 914 and 838

a) 6

b) If the current year is 2004, then the comet Denning-Fujikawa will have been seen 13 times.

Challenge

Answers will vary.

Multiplication

a) £248.30

b) 13 kg

c) £39

a) £28,800

b) £937.72

Challenge

£179.40

Division

a) 100 coach loads

b) £80

c) £45

a) 6 minutes

b) £12.50

Challenge
£8,928.57

2D shapes

a) 4

b) A trapezium

c) Equilateral triangle
(3 sides) and
parallelogram (4 sides)

a) 12

b) 24

Challenge

x	h	e	p	t	a	g	o	n	l	a	w	e	r	y
p	f	b	a	d	p	e	n	t	a	g	o	n	p	u
y	g	h	p	a	z	q	d	i	a	g	o	n	a	l
i	k	s	d	r	b	u	j	s	z	m	c	e	r	r
s	e	c	j	k	c	i	r	c	l	e	t	q	a	h
q	u	a	d	r	i	l	a	t	e	r	a	l	l	o
u	i	l	e	a	q	a	t	r	a	d	g	p	l	m
a	v	e	t	u	o	t	k	i	t	e	o	o	e	b
r	u	n	g	r	h	e	x	a	g	o	n	l	l	u
e	q	e	g	d	z	r	u	n	o	h	l	y	o	s
s	o	r	e	c	t	a	n	g	l	e	c	g	g	c
t	p	a	r	a	l	l	e	l	e	f	s	o	r	l
b	m	u	i	s	o	s	c	e	l	e	s	n	a	j
f	a	b	u	t	r	a	p	e	z	i	u	m	m	h

3D shapes

a) Cones

b) Square-based pyramid and hemisphere

c) Octahedron

a) 12. Dodecahedron

b) 25 and 5

Challenge

Shape	cubes	cuboids	square-based pyramids	spheres	hemispheres	cylinders
Number	27	1	3	1	2	4
Shape	cones	prisms	tetrahedrons	polyhedrons	octahedrons	dodecahedrons
Number	3	2	2	7	4	1

Position and direction

a) (4, −4), (4, −6), (6, −4) and (6, −6)

b) Swimming (hopefully!)

c) (−6, 4), (−6, 6) and (−4, 6) or (4, 6), (6, 6) and
(6, 4)

a) (−2, −3), (−2, −1), (−5, −1) and (−5, 2)

b) (−4, −6), (−6, −6), (−6, −4) and (−4, −4)

Challenge
Answers will vary.

Data handling

a) 1–10
b) 21–30
c) 20

a) 44
b) 68

Challenge
Graph should show a bias towards the younger age brackets.

Two-step problems

a) £54
b) £6.75
c) There are 68 sweets left. They made £15.32.

a) 102 sponges were thrown
b) £28.50

Challenge
3 ducks

Your notes